Grade 3

The Syllabus of Examinations should be read for details of requirements, especially those for scales, aural tests and sight-reading. Attention should be paid to the Special Notices on the front inside cover, where warning is given of changes.

The syllabus is obtainable from music dealers or from The Associated Board of the Royal Schools of Music, 14 Bedford Square, London WC1B 3JG (please send a stamped addressed envelope measuring about 9 × 6 ins.).

In overseas centres, information may be obtained from the Local Representative or Resident Secretary.

Requirements

SCALES, ARPEGGIOS AND BROKEN CHORDS (from memory)

Scales
(i) in similar motion, hands together one octave apart, and each hand separately, in the following keys:
A, E, B, B♭, E♭ majors and B, G, C minors
(melodic *or* harmonic minor at candidate's choice)
(all two octaves)
(ii) in contrary motion, both hands beginning and ending on the key-note (unison), in the keys of A and E♭ majors (two octaves)

Chromatic Scales
each hand separately, beginning on A♭, B and C (two octaves)

Arpeggios
the common chords of A, E, B, B♭ and E♭ majors, and B, G and C minors, in root position only, each hand separately (two octaves)

Broken Chords
formed from the chords of G and F majors, and E and D minors, each hand separately, according to either of the patterns shown in the syllabus at candidate's choice

PLAYING AT SIGHT (see current syllabus)

AURAL TESTS (see current syllabus)

THREE PIECES

Candidates must prepare Nos.1 & 2 from the *same* list, A *or* B, but may choose No.3 from *either* list *or* one of the further alternatives listed below:

Cui Shy Confession, Op.20 No.2
Swinstead In The Bay
These are included in More Romantic Pieces for Piano, Book II, *published by the Associated Board*

Printed in Great Britain by Headley Brothers Ltd, The Invicta Press, Ashford, Kent and London

Copyright pieces in this publication are printed as issued by the copyright owners and are reproduced with their permission.

Other pieces have been checked with original source material and edited as necessary for instructional purposes. Fingering, phrasing, pedalling, metronome marks and the editorial realization of ornaments (where given) are for guidance but are not comprehensive or obligatory. Any good alternatives, which are appropriate in style, will be accepted by the examiners.

A:1
PRELUDE in C

Edited by
Richard Jones

Attributed to J.S. BACH, BWV 939

The first of four Preludes attributed to Bach in a mid-18th-century MS. Ornaments in bar 7 and bars 10-11 and the slur and small notes at the final cadence are editorial suggestions only. The opening right-hand phrase (bars 1-4) might be subdivided into three shorter units, each beginning on the second quaver of the bar and breaking after the first note of the next bar; this phrasing would then be applied throughout the piece. The original had no dynamics and those offered are editorial suggestions only.

Reprinted from J.S. Bach, *A Little Keyboard Book*, edited by Richard Jones (Associated Board)

A:2
SONATA in A flat
Second movement

Edited by
Howard Ferguson

HAYDN, Hob.XVI/43

Source: an early copyist's MS titled *Sonata per Cembalo. Di Gius. Hayden*, in the Staatsbibliothek Preussischer Kulturbesitz in Berlin. All dynamics are editorial. Some articulation marks have been added on the basis of those given by Haydn in parallel passages. Wedges indicate *staccato*.

Reprinted from Haydn, *Selected Keyboard Sonatas*, Book II, edited by Howard Ferguson (Associated Board)

Menuetto 2do

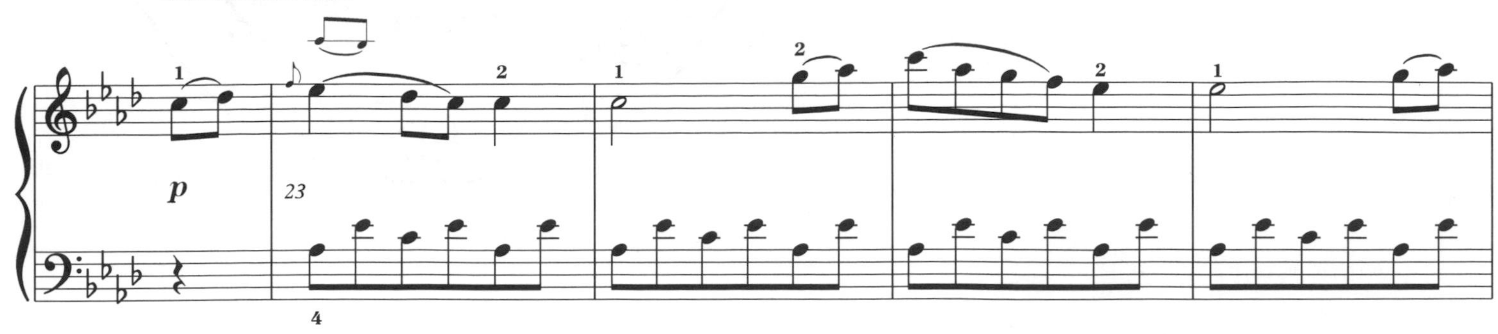

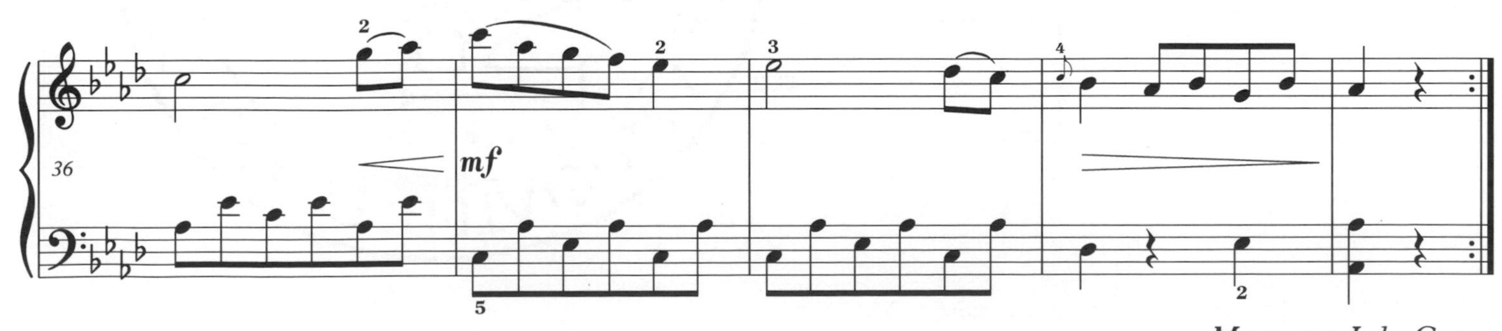

Menuetto I da Capo

A:3

AUTUMN WIND

from 'Easy Pieces'

STANISLAW PRÓSZYŃSKI

Moderato [♩ = *c*.104]

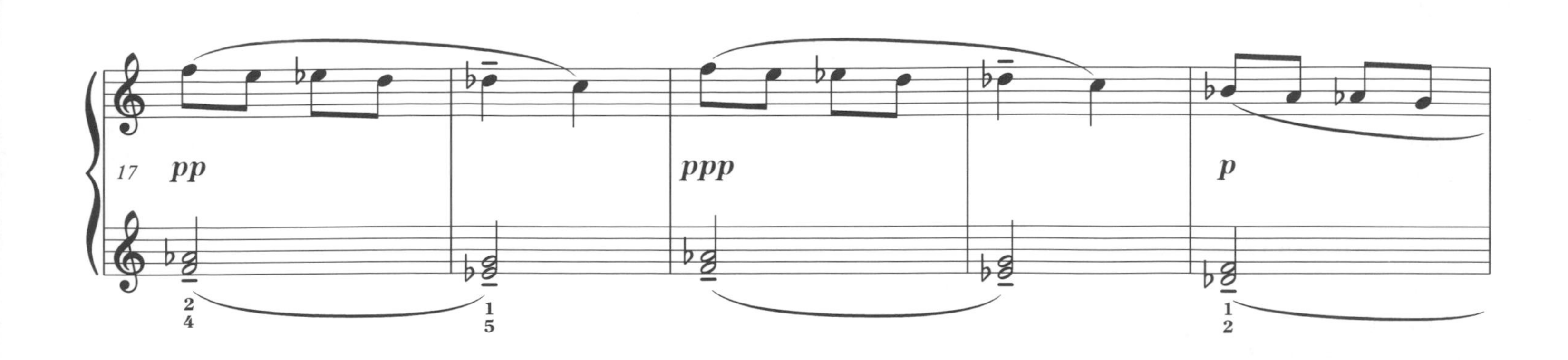
17
pp
ppp
p

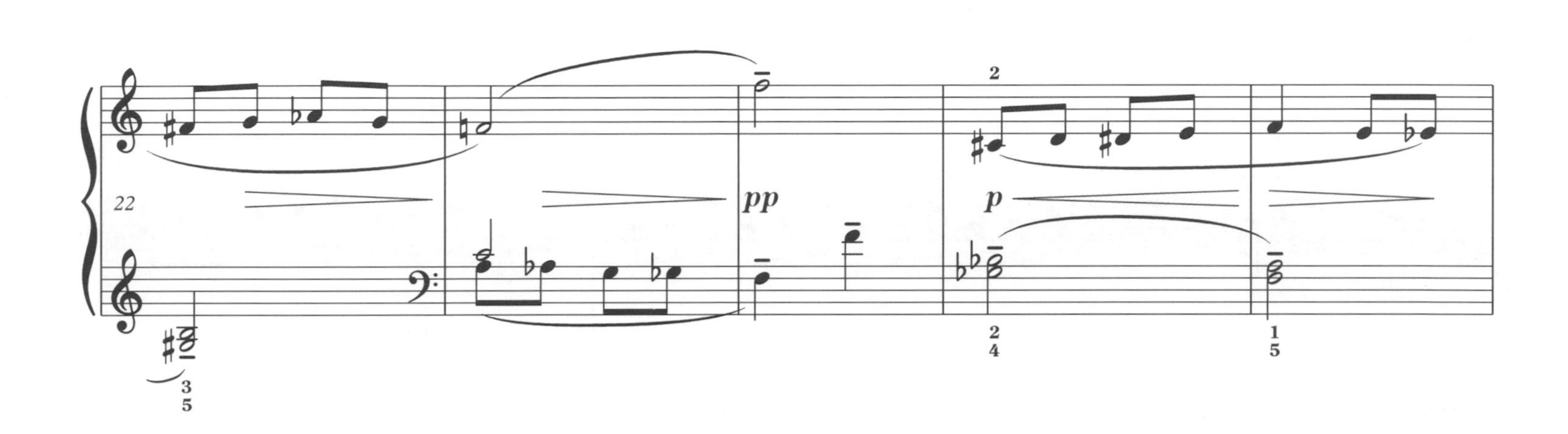
22
pp
p

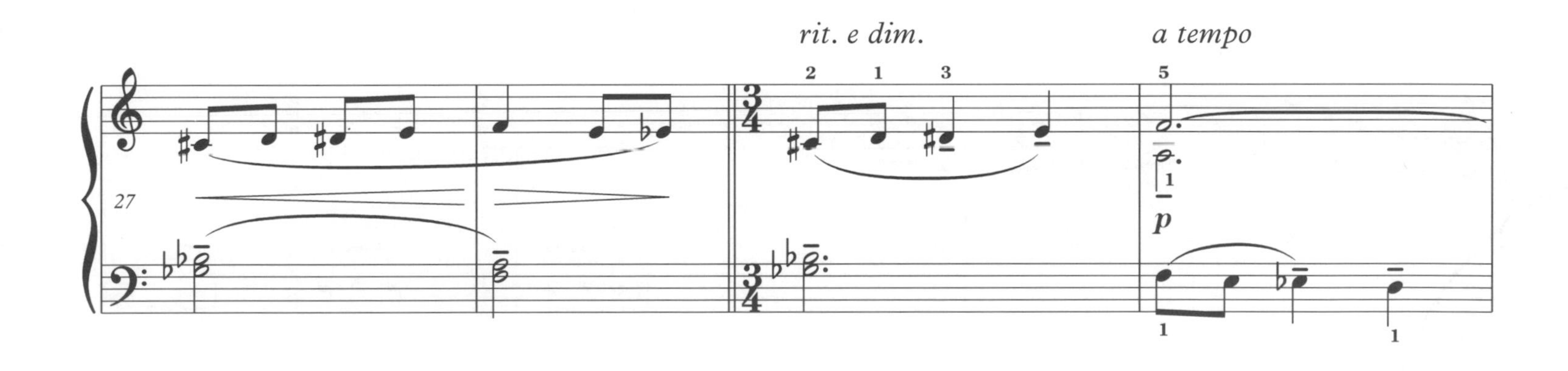
rit. e dim.
a tempo
27
p

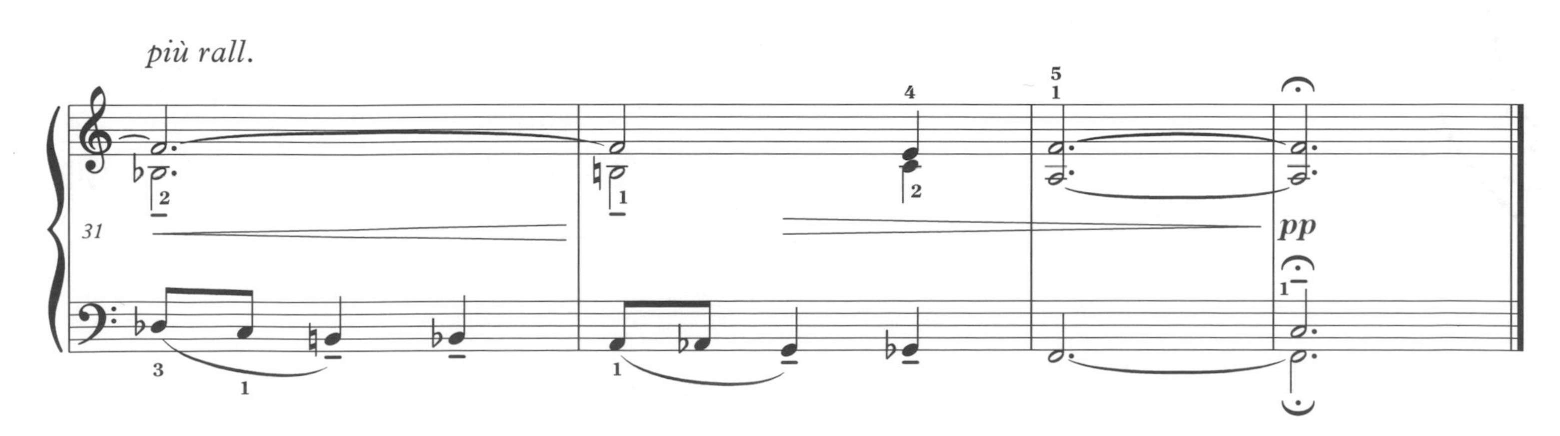
più rall.
31
pp

B:1
ALLEGRO in F

Edited by
Timothy Roberts

HUMMEL

Reprinted from Hummel, *Sixteen Short Pieces*, edited by Timothy Roberts (Associated Board)

Hummel was an outstanding contemporary of Beethoven, famed throughout Europe as a virtuoso pianist and improviser. This piece is No.56 of his *Klavierschule*, a massive piano tutor printed in 1828. Dynamics are original, except for the *diminuendi* in bars 4, 8 and 12 and the ***p*** in bar 14. Some articulation marks have been added on the basis of those given in parallel passages in the original. The *staccato* dot on the first right-hand note of bar 17 might be applied to the first chords of bars 17-20, both hands.

B:3*

TIP-TOE TANGO

PHILIP CANNON

Tip-Toe Tango is from *Jazz and Blues*, Volume 3, by Philip Cannon.

* B:3 precedes B:2 in order to avoid a page turn in the former.

pp
f
pp
mf
p
p
mf

B:2
STUDY in A flat

CZERNY, Op.139 No.51

Czerny was reportedly able to play the piano by the age of 3 and, after becoming Beethoven's pupil, made his public début in Vienna at the age of 10. He later taught many of the great 19th-century piano virtuosi, including Liszt. He wrote a prodigious amount of instructional pieces for the piano.